We He
the Ga

By Janice Behrens

ISBN: 978-1-338-88860-7

Editor: Liza Charlesworth
Art Director: Tannaz Fassihi; Designer: Tanya Chernyak
Photos ©: 3: A3pfamily/Shutterstock.com.; 6: kochabamba/Shutterstock.com.
All other photos © Getty Images.

SCHOLASTIC INC.

I get to dig the dirt.
Is that the best job?

I get to plant the flowers.
Is that the best job?

I get to carry the flowers.
Is that the best job?

I get to water the flowers.
Is that the best job?

I get to paint the fence.
Is that the best job?

I get to pick the carrots.
Is that the best job?

I get to eat the carrots.
Is that the best job?
Yes, it is!